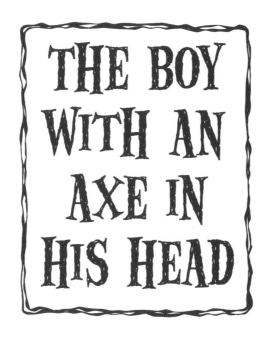

THE BOY WITH AN AXE IN HIS HEAD

Peter Underhill

starfish
imprint

This book is dedicated to my lovely wife Dawn
and our son Lewis, to whom I offer my gratitude
for their infinite patience as passengers on my
journey to creative contentment.
We'll get there one day - I promise.

First published in 2008 by Starfish Imprint, Mitre House, School Road, Bulkington, Warwickshire CV12 9JB.
Starfish Imprint is a trading name of Chocolate Starfish Limited of the same address.

2 4 6 8 10 9 7 5 3 1

All text and illustrations © Peter Underhill

www.peterunderhill.com

The right of Peter Underhill to be identified as author and illustrator of this work has been
asserted by him in accordance with the Copyright, Designs and Patents Act 1988.

This book has been typeset in Fink Condensed.

Printed in the Hong Kong.

ISBN 978-0-9557666-0-2

This is Maxwell Whitbread, just a normal kid.
No-one cared who he was, or even what he did.
He wasn't all that good at stuff, but wasn't really bad.
He was just an average kid, but ginger, like his dad.

On a trip from school one day, to a home, so very stately,
He saw a suit of armour that had not been dusted lately.
"A shame" thought Max to himself, "but if I use my sleeve,
I think that I might polish it, just before I leave".

Breathing on the dusty steel, its lustre to improve,
As Max began to buff the suit, its axe began to move.
Standing to admire his work, the metal looking good,
He didn't see the axe until it hit him with a thud!

The battle axe was heavy, it did its job too well.
It almost split his head in two, and to the ground he fell.
Rushing to the poor boy's aid, the teachers thought him dead,
Lying on the parquet floor, an axe stuck in his head.

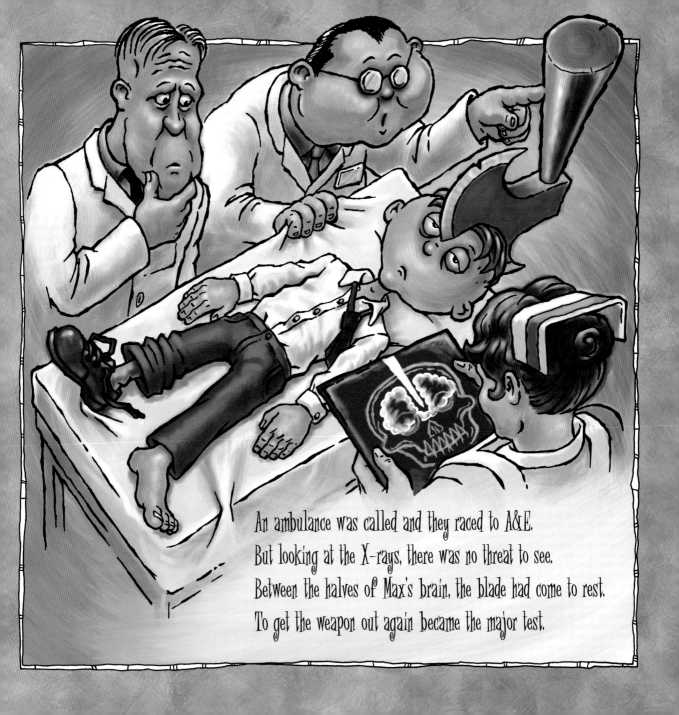

An ambulance was called and they raced to A&E.
But looking at the X-rays, there was no threat to see.
Between the halves of Max's brain, the blade had come to rest.
To get the weapon out again became the major test.

So they set to work extracting the hunk of steel and wood.
But to remove the axe of war, they really were no good.
They pulled and pushed and heaved and hoed and even gave a nudge,
But the massive battle axe, it simply wouldn't budge.

As the doctors could do nought and Max was in no pain,
The only thing that they could do was send him home again.
So with a dab of ointment, they sent him on his way,
But Max was yet to realise how life would change that day.

ACCIDENT &
EMERGENCY

From someone so ignorable,
Max became well known.
Everybody stared at him,
He'd never be alone.
As the playground 'nobody',
He'd blend into the crowd.
Imagine school assemblies,
With an axe that stood out proud.

The benefits, Max soon found out, were plentiful and wide,
But balancing the happy things, there was a darker side.
With every bonus that the axe had added to his life,
There grew a brooding darkness that caused him endless strife.

When going to the shops, his friends they quickly found,
That Max's handle could reach up much higher from the ground.
Knocking things from higher up than they could reach before,
Sometimes fragile items though, came crashing to the floor.

Max liked playing football, but one thing deeply hurt,
He wasn't picked for either team, neither skin nor shirt.
He'd be called onto the pitch, but that's when things got bad.
They used him as a goalpost, which made him really sad.

When school held a Sports Day, Max did really well.
At pole vaulting and baseball, and rounders he'd excel.
He also joined a fencing club to buckle and to swash,
Which won him lots of prizes and pockets full of dosh.

When it rains on washdays, for many it's a pain,
But Maxell came in handy when it poured down with rain.
Mrs Whitbread didn't need a modern tumble drier,
She simply sat young Maxwell closer to the fire.

Max's sister Eunice, off school with chicken pox,
Couldn't find a thing to do in all of her toy box.
So, to prevent his sister from becoming bored,
Maxwell made a swing for her, and to the sky she soared.

His friends tried different hairstyles, but Maxwell didn't care.
He hardly had a choice on where to part his hair.
With fashion though, Maxwell would wear the latest pants,
But wearing trendy headgear, he didn't stand a chance.

On visiting a pool hall, Max showed natural flair.
He used his handle as a cue and no-one seemed to care.
When playing against champions, he proved more than able,
But it got pretty boring when he'd always clear the table.

On a fated boat trip with uncle Frank one day,
The rudder broke clean off the boat, with Max, they found a way.
Plunged into the chilly brine, a tube for him to breathe,
Once back on terra firma, Max swore he'd never leave.

Max liked reading scary books,
Especially late at night.
He found a really useful place
From where to hang his light.
He'd read some HP Lovecraft
And Edgar Allan Poe,
Then spend all night in fear
Of beyond the lantern's glow.

Maxwell joined a fishing club, but often fished alone.
Others seeing him arrive, would pack up and go home.
"Just for once, if he could fail" was their dearest wish.
It wasn't really Max's fault he'd haul out all the fish.

The years rolled by and Maxwell tried to find some paying work.
He wasn't very qualified, but wasn't one to shirk.
He walked into a burger bar and found that work was there.
At flipping burgers all day long, no-one could compare.

So many things in Max's life had changed now for the good,
From being hit by a lump of steel and a length of wood.
From sports right through to cookery, his skills had surely grown,
But despite a full social life, he always felt alone.

Nobody knew what it was like for Max to be unique.
Where once he was invisible, now he felt a freak.
All his friends had partners, with whom to bill and coo,
Max went home to nobody, and meals for one, not two.

Wedding Invite

He slipped into a deep despair, a dark and lonely place,
And went for endless walks so that no-one saw his face.
One day when at his bleakest, a walk took him afar,
A distant place unseen before, unreachable by car.

Towards him on this lonely road, began a distant speck,
He saw a girl out walking, a thing stuck from her neck.
Then, as they drew closer, he saw her pretty face.
He had the strangest feeling, his heart began to race.

Standing still the pair of them, their mouths both hung agape.
He saw the sickle through her neck, from front right through to nape.
An obvious connection, here on a country lane,
Fate brought them together, both different, yet the same.

Maxwell begged to know her name, "Primrose" she replied.
They knew they had a future, that couldn't be denied.
So off they went together, both glad to have a friend.
They walked towards the sunset, but that's not quite the end.

They both found work in forestry and built a house from logs,
And filled it up with parakeets and a pair of scruffy dogs.
Growing old and happy, they lived in forest glades,
Tending to the undergrowth by using both their blades.

If you go down to the woods, a swishing sound you hear,
Don't go feeling frightened, no monster's drawing near.
Nor vampire bats searching for necks on which to feed.
It's simply Max and Primrose trimming back the weeds.

The End.

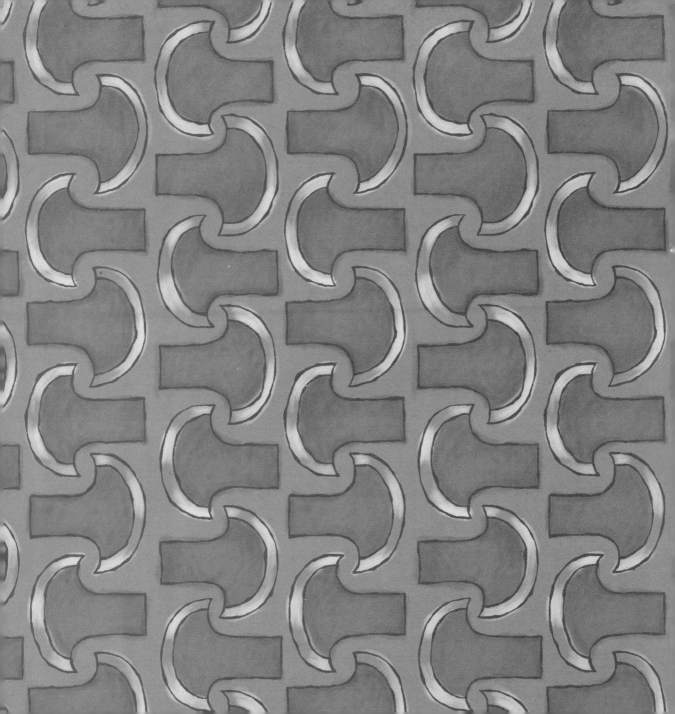